CREATIVE
COLOURING
FOR GROWN-UPS

Glorious Gardens

Michael O'Mara Books Limited

First published in Great Britain in 2014
This flexiback edition first published in 2015 by
Michael O'Mara Books Limited
9 Lion Yard
Tremadoc Road
London SW4 7NQ

A CIP catalogue record for this book is available from the British Library.

Papers used by Michael O'Mara Books Limited are natural, recyclable
products made from wood grown in sustainable forests. The manufacturing
processes conform to the environmental regulations of the country of
origin.

ISBN: 978-1-78243-500-6

1 2 3 4 5 6 7 8 9 10

www.mombooks.com

Designed by Billy Waqar
Cover by Claire Cater

Illustrations by Sally Moret, Hannah Davies, Greg Stevenson, Iván Cruz,
Ale Abuelita, Jay Raine and Shutterstock.com

Printed and bound in China

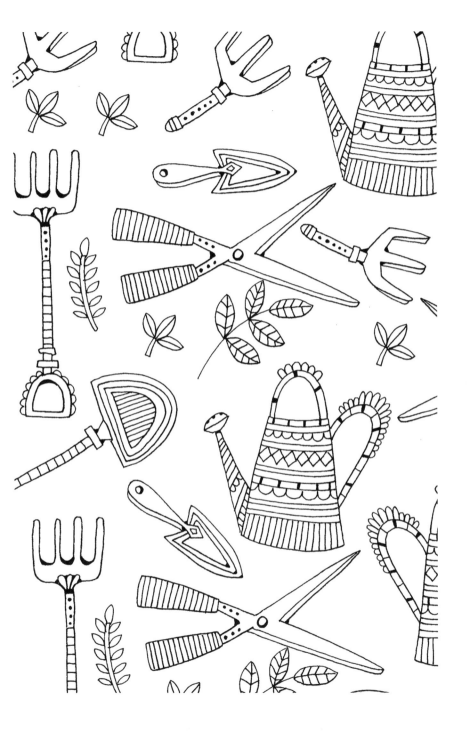

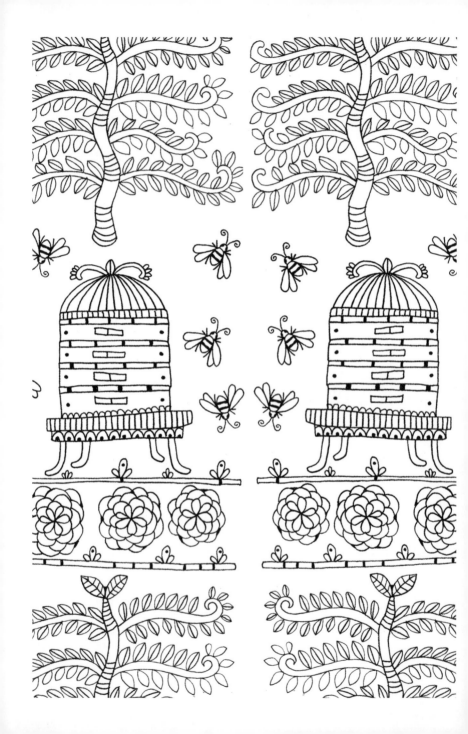

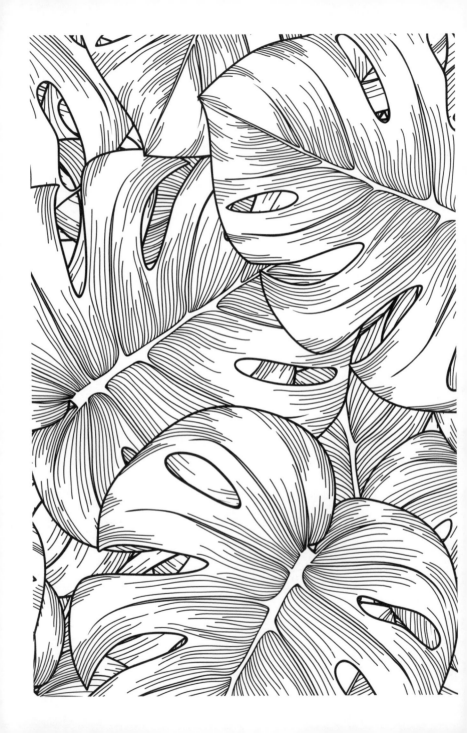